Picture Prompts
FOR WRITING

by Linda Schwartz

Illustrated by Corbyn Kern

2003 / The Learning Works

This book is dedicated to my special friend and mentee,
Karen Lopez.

The Learning Works

Illustrator: Corbyn Kern
Book design: Studio E Books, Santa Barbara, CA
Cover illustrator: Corbyn Kern
Cover designer: Barbara Peterson
Project director: Linda Schwartz

Special thanks to Ellen Goldman, Bev Armstrong, Bobbie Vidal, and Sue Perona for their valuable feedback and suggestions.

Contents

To the Teacher

Picture Prompts for Writing is a creative tool to motivate students to write about people, places, things, and feelings. In each exercise, a drawing is presented along with a wide variety of writing prompts for short stories, essays, and poetry. Students can choose any of the ideas listed with each drawing as a springboard to writing. Most importantly, the writing prompts are correlated to the standards established for writing and will help prepare students for the written component of standardized tests (see page 5).

The format is extremely flexible. Students can work alone or with partners, and the activities can be done in any order. The pictures and writing prompts are ideal to post at learning centers, to use for extra credit or homework assignments, or to offer to students who complete their classwork ahead of others.

Many of the prompts in this book emphasize narrative writing based on students' personal experiences. Others provide practice in writing short stories and essays so that students can build skills in developing characters, establishing settings, and structuring plots. They provide students with essential practice in incorporating all of the elements that go into good writing. The use of sensory details such as how things look, sound, smell, taste, and feel are emphasized in the writing prompts. Students will also have an opportunity to use personification, similes, and metaphors to enhance their writing.

Ask students to read their finished stories aloud to themselves and to proofread, edit, and revise their work. To help them, a list of proofreader's symbols and a writing checklist are provided on the inside front cover and on page 80, respectively.

Students will become better writers the more they write. *Picture Prompts for Writing* provides you with lots of ready-to-use creative ideas correlated to today's writing standards to get them started.

Writing Standards

Many of the writing prompts in this book have been correlated to the following basic writing standards.

Write narratives
a. Relate ideas, observations, or recollections of an event or experience.
b. Provide a context to enable the reader to imagine the world of the event or experience.
c. Use concrete sensory details.
d. Establish a plot, point of view, setting, and conflict.
e. Provide insight into why the selected event or experience is memorable.

Create multiple-paragraph expository compositions
a. Establish a topic and give important ideas or events in sequence or chronological order.
b. Provide details and transitional expressions that link one paragraph to another in a clear line of thought.

Write information reports
a. Frame a central question about an issue or situation.
b. Include facts and details for focus.
c. Draw from more than one source of information.

Write persuasive letters or compositions
a. State a clear position in support of a proposal.
b. Support a position with relevant evidence.
c. Follow a simple organizational pattern.

The following language skills are incorporated into most of the writing prompts:

Sentence structure
a. Use simple and compound sentences in writing.
b. Combine short related sentences with appositives, participial phrases, adjectives, adverbs, and prepositional phrases.

Grammar
a. Identify and use regular and irregular verbs, adjectives, prepositions, and coordinating conjunctions.

Punctuation
a. Use parentheses, commas in direct quotations, and apostrophes in the possessive case of nouns and in contractions.
b. Use underlining, quotation marks, or italics to identify titles of documents.

Capitalization
a. Capitalize the names of magazines, newspapers, works of art, musical compositions, organizations, and the first words in quotations when appropriate.

Spelling
a. Spell correctly roots, inflections, suffixes, and prefixes.

Friends

Write a three-way conversation among the friends in the picture. Are they talking about the big game coming up this weekend, a humorous thing that happened to one of them, or an unusual event?

Write a short story about these friends. Give them names and describe their physical characteristics and personalities. One of the settings of your story should be the one pictured.

Write the first chapter of a story involving two friends who set out to solve a mystery. Develop a strong plot, setting, and characters.

Write a humorous story about friends who find themselves in a hilarious predicament.

What qualities do you look for in a friend? Write a one-page exposition in which you describe the characteristics you think a friend should have.

Write about a time you and a friend had a major disagreement. Describe the events that led up to the problem. Was it ever resolved?

Write a narrative about one of the nicest things a friend ever did for you or one of the best things you ever did for a friend.

Write a cinquain poem about friendship. Your poem should have five lines and follow this structure:

    line 1: one word of two syllables (the title of your poem)
    line 2: four syllables (describing the word on line 1)
    line 3: six syllables (showing action)
    line 4: eight syllables (expressing a feeling or observation about the subject)
    line 5: two syllables (describing the subject)

Friends

The Parade

Choose one of the people watching the parade, and write about his or her feelings. Use sensory details to describe the sights and sounds he or she experiences. Capture the excitement of the parade as it passes by this viewer.

Imagine that one of these people is blind. Describe the parade as that person perceives it.

Choose one of the adults in the picture and imagine that watching the parade stirs up memories from his or her past. Write a story about what is going through his or her mind. What words would best describe this person's emotions? Are other people included? If so, tell who they are and what roles they play.

Imagine that you are a clown in the parade. As you pass this group of people, one of them catches your eye. What made you notice him or her?

Write a descriptive paragraph capturing all the colors of the parade. Paint a rainbow of bright, eye-catching hues in your paragraph.

Imagine that you are a photographer who has been hired to write a human interest story about the parade. Choose one of the people watching the parade, and write something about him or her that will stir the emotions of your readers.

Write a paragraph describing the music a marching band plays as it passes by. Isolate the sounds made by the different instruments, and use colorful words to compare and contrast them.

9

The Parade

The Marathon Runner

Imagine you are the runner in front, crossing the finish line of a grueling marathon. Describe your thoughts at the moment you finish the race. Make people who read your writing feel as if they are right there with you.

Write four or more journal entries in the diary of this runner. Describe what motivated him to enter the race. Describe the highs and lows of his training for the marathon. What personal sacrifices did he have to make to prepare himself for the race?

Imagine that you are a spectator on the sidelines watching the runner cross the finish line. Describe the thoughts going through your mind. How do you compare yourself to this runner? Would you want to trade places with him at this moment? Would you have the desire or stamina to train for a marathon?

Describe a time you set a physical challenge for yourself through sports, a job, or a service project. What motivated you to set this goal? Did you finish what you set out to accomplish? What did you learn about yourself?

Write a sports story based on a sport you enjoy. Pick an incident that actually happened to you while playing, or make up a fictional event. Include at least two other major characters in your story, and write dialogue among the three of you.

 Most marathons include competitors in wheelchairs. Do research to see what you can learn about these athletes who compete in marathons. Then imagine that you are participating in a marathon in a wheelchair. Describe the highlights of the race, including the reaction of people cheering you on from the sidelines, the huge crowds, and the final moment when you cross the finish line. How would things be different for a wheelchair-bound competitor?

The Marathon Runner

Lunch with a Friend

Imagine a topic that both groups of friends are talking about such as a friend or family member, a pet, a book, a trip or travel plans, or shopping. Write several paragraphs of the conversation the two older women are having on the topic you selected. Then write the dialogue that the three teens are having on the same subject.

Imagine that the two older women are talking about the teenage girls sitting across from them. What are they saying? Write several paragraphs of their conversation.

Imagine that the three teenage girls are talking about the women sitting behind them. What are they saying? Write several paragraphs of their conversation.

Write a paragraph in which you compare and contrast the two groups of friends. Include ways in which they are alike in the way they dress, talk, think, and/or act, and ways in which they are different.

Imagine that both sets of friends are talking about the best age to be. If you could listen in on both of their conversations, what would you hear each pair say?

Describe the food that one of these people has ordered for lunch. Use sensory details to describe the smell, taste, feel, and appearance of the food. Make your description so vivid that someone reading your paragraph will actually get hungry.

Write a narrative based on a special meal you had with a close friend. Relate your recollections of this meal you shared, what you ate, what you talked about, what you felt.

Imagine that each set of friends is discussing events in the news. Write dialogue expressing their views of current events.

Lunch with a Friend

The Bus Stop

Imagine that you are related to one of the three people shown waiting for the bus in the picture. Write a paragraph describing this person in detail—his or her physical characteristics, personality, strengths, weaknesses, likes and dislikes, etc. Reveal something about the person that very few people know—even those very close to him or her.

Write a short story with one of these three people as the main character. Give him or her a name. Establish a plot, point of view, setting, and conflict. Your story should reveal the events that brought this person to the bus stop and give the reader clues about where he or she is going.

Using sensory details, write a descriptive paragraph in which you capture the sights and sounds surrounding the bus stop through the eyes of one of the three people waiting for the bus. You can place your bus stop along a busy city street, near a public park, on a country road, or anywhere you want.

Imagine that you are one of the three people at the bus stop. While waiting for the bus, you start daydreaming. Your thoughts turn back in time to an important event in your life. Write an essay about your thoughts and how this important event affected your life.

Pick any two of the people at the bus stop, and imagine that they start a conversation to help pass the time while waiting for the bus. Write the dialogue that takes place between them until the bus arrives.

Imagine that you are the elderly woman in the picture. Write a narrative describing your thoughts about the teenager who is waiting with you at the bus stop. Compare him to someone you remember from your youth.

Imagine that you are the bus stop bench. Using personification, describe the most unusual person who ever sat on you while waiting for the bus.

15

The Bus Stop

Grandma

Write a story about the grandmother and her granddaughter in the picture. Describe the setting and what brought them to this place. In your story, share something special that the child learns from her grandmother. What does the grandmother learn from her granddaughter?

Write an essay describing a special time you shared with your grandmother or something you learned from her that you remember to this day.

How would you describe your grandmother (or grandfather) to someone else? Write an essay and describe her (or his) physical characteristics and personality. What are her special talents and strengths? What makes her happy? What are some of her concerns and fears?

Discover more about your grandmother. Talk to her about what life was like when she was your age. Write an essay in which you compare and contrast her early life to yours. Some of the things you might want to explore include her

      home life
      school
      friends
      chores and family responsibilities
      favorite games
      trips and vacations

What other new things can you learn about your grandmother?

Do you have a special name for your grandmother? If so, write a story about how she got her nickname.

Write a poem about your grandmother, grandfather, or another relative. Your poem does not have to rhyme.

For all the ideas above, feel free to write about your grandfather, aunt, uncle, or another adult friend or relative.

Grandma

The Checkers Game

Who are the two people in this picture? Are they strangers, or are they related to each other? Write a short story and make the checkers game an integral part of the setting or plot.

What is your favorite board game? Imagine you are explaining this game to someone who is not familiar with it. Write a description of the object and rules of the game.

Write an essay about something important you learned from an older person. This thing you learned could be a lesson about life, a hobby or craft, a game or sport, or whatever you choose. Describe how, where, and when you learned this lesson. Tell how this knowledge has had an effect on your life.

What is the origin of the game of checkers? Write a research report and include facts and details about checkers (or any other game that interests you). Use more than one source of information.

Imagine that you are a red or black checker in this game. Using personification, describe what your life is like as you move around the board and strive to become a king.

Write a short story about a game or sport at which you have competed. Include details about your opponent(s), the setting of the game, and the feelings you experienced during and after the game or competition.

The Checkers Game

An Immigrant Family

Write an adventure story about this immigrant family that came to America in search of a better way of life. Describe some of the hardships they endured and obstacles they overcame to realize their dreams.

Write one chapter of a historical novel using the picture as a springboard. Do research on the homes, dress, food, and leisure activities of this period in history to make your chapter authentic.

Imagine you are the boy in the picture. Write a one-page journal entry describing something unusual and exciting that happened while traveling by boat to America.

Imagine you are the mother or father in the picture. Write about your feelings concerning bringing your family to a strange country. What worries you the most? What do you want for your children?

Write an informational report on immigration. Frame a central question about the issue, and include facts and details for focus. Use two or more sources of information.

Imagine you are one of the people in this family. You are lying awake at night, unable to sleep on the voyage across the sea to America. Use sensory details to describe the sights, smells, and sounds that surround you.

Where do your ancestors come from? Talk to your mom or dad and learn more about your family's history. Write a short story based on a relative who came to this country from a foreign land.

In what ways is your life similar to that of the boy in the picture? In what ways is it different? In which period of time would you rather live? Explain your answer.

An Immigrant Family

Bag Lady

Write a detailed description of the woman in this picture. Describe her facial features, her clothing, posture, personality, etc.

Write an essay describing the woman's cart and the significance of its contents.

Imagine that you are homeless. Describe three vivid memories of places you've spent the night or things you have seen on the street. Use sensory details to evoke a sense of place.

Imagine you are the woman in the picture. Write a paragraph describing what you see in the eyes of strangers who pass you on the street.

Imagine that you are an undercover police officer dressed as a bag lady while on assignment to capture a robber last seen in the neighborhood. Write a story about how you nab the robber while dressed as a bag lady. Develop a strong plot, setting, and main character.

Imagine that you are a reporter for a local newspaper. You have been assigned to document a day in the life of a homeless person. Pick one hour of a day, and write what you observe as you live alongside a homeless man or woman.

Write an essay explaining your ideas about what steps should be taken to help the homeless in your community.

Write a story about a homeless person who buys a lottery ticket and ends up winning a multimillion-dollar jackpot.

Write a research report about homeless people in your community or in a large city. Start by framing a central question about the issue, and include facts and details for focus. Use at least two sources of information.

Bag Lady

You

Describe the person you see when you look in a mirror. What do you like best about what you see?

 Describe yourself through the eyes of a family member—your mom, dad, sister, brother, grandparent, or other relative. What would this person say are your greatest strengths and weaknesses?

Think about what your life might be like ten years from now. Where would you like to be living? What would you like to be doing? Write about your ideas.

Imagine that a Hollywood movie producer wants to make a movie about your life. Write a paragraph describing what famous actor or actress you would suggest casting for the role of you and who you would select to portray the important people in your life. Tell why you selected each one.

Write one chapter of your autobiography. Describe a memorable incident, the funniest thing that ever happened to you, your most embarrassing moment, or a person who has greatly influenced your life.

Describe your favorite clothes to wear when it's time to kick back and relax. Write a second description of something you would wear to a formal occasion.

If you could be any animal, which one would you be? Tell why you choose to be this animal.

Write a narrative about someone you admire. Describe how that person has affected your life. Compare and contrast this person with someone else you know.

Write a poem about yourself in which each line has exactly two words. Your poem does not have to rhyme.

25

You

At the Beach

Who is the person in this picture? What brought him or her to this setting? Describe this person's mood. What does this person's silhouette tell you? As this person gazes out to sea, what thoughts pass through his or her mind?

Imagine you are strolling along this beach. Using sensory details, describe the feel of the sand and water as you walk barefoot along the ocean's edge.

Imagine you are walking along this beach and meet the person pictured. You stop to talk to him or her for a few minutes. Write dialogue for the conversation the two of you have.

Write an essay about a day you spent at a beach, lake, or river. Use sensory details to describe the setting, and tell what you saw, felt, smelled, tasted, and heard. What patterns or textures in nature did you observe? Use adverbs and adjectives to make your description vivid and realistic.

Imagine that you see a bottle bob among the incoming waves and wash up onto the shore. You go over to investigate and notice a piece of paper rolled inside the bottle. You pull out the note and read it. Who wrote the note, and to whom was it written? What does it say? What action, if any, do you take?

Write a short story about a rescue at sea using this beach as your setting. Make the excitement and suspense mount to grab and hold your reader's attention.

Write a poem about a beach, the ocean, a sunrise, or a sunset. Your poem does not have to rhyme.

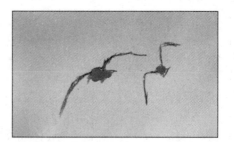

At the Beach

The Stadium

Choose one of the people in this picture and write about the stadium through that person's eyes. Use sensory details to capture the setting and the emotions of the people sitting near you.

Describe the ballpark through the eyes of the hot dog vendor. Use sensory details to describe the colors, sounds, and smells he observes.

What are the two boys talking about during the game? Write the dialogue between them.

Imagine that you are the father with the young son. This is your son's first trip to the stadium. Watching the game brings back all kinds of memories of your childhood and your visits to the stadium with your own father. Write an essay describing one memorable game you watched with your dad.

Write a sports story that takes place during a World Series game. Describe the final play that wins or loses the game for one of the teams.

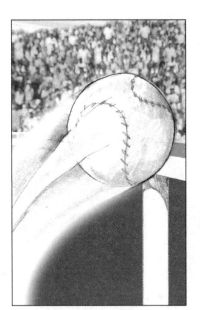

Imagine this same stadium late at night, after the game is over and all the fans have left for home. Picture yourself standing at home plate. Write a paragraph that captures the setting and mood of the moment.

Imagine that you are one of the players on the field. You look up into the bleachers and scan the faces of the crowd. Describe the thoughts that run through your head.

29

The Stadium

Your Home

Imagine that you are looking out a window of your home. What room are you in? Describe what you see from the window during the day. What sounds can you hear outside?

Describe a favorite room in your home—the kitchen, family room, living room, dining room, or any room you wish. How is the room furnished? What colors are used? What makes this room special?

If you could start over and completely redecorate your bedroom or the place you sleep, describe what you would do. Would you pick a theme related to a special hobby or interest? What would you put in your room to make it uniquely yours?

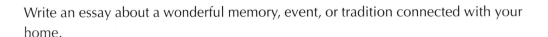

Imagine that a person is walking by your home and looks in the living room window. Describe the scene the person would see. Who in your family would be there? What would they be talking about or doing?

Write an essay about a wonderful memory, event, or tradition connected with your home.

Dinner's cooking, and something smells fantastic! Use sensory details to describe the aroma coming from the kitchen as you walk in the front door after your afternoon soccer practice.

Write a research report on one of the following types of homes:

> geodesic dome
> igloo
> sod cabin
> solar house
> wigwam
> yurt

Include facts and details about the home you select. Use two or more sources of information.

Have you ever lived somewhere other than where you live now? If so, compare that home with your current home. What are the advantages and disadvantages of each?

Your Home

The Movie Theater

Imagine that you are one of the five people waiting in line to buy a ticket to the movie. Write in first person, and describe what happens as you walk into the dark theater and try to find a seat after the movie has already started.

Imagine that you are a film critic for a newspaper. Write a review of a movie you've recently seen. Tell your readers enough about the movie to pique their interest, but don't give away the ending.

Describe the worst movie you ever saw.

Imagine that you are a writer for a teen magazine and have been asked to arrange an interview with a famous actor or actress. Decide who you want to interview, and make a list of ten questions you would ask this celebrity during your time together. Make up answers you think you'd get.

Use sensory details to describe sitting inside a darkened movie theater. What do you see on the screen? What sounds can you hear? What aromas can you smell?

What makes seeing a movie in a theater different from watching a video at home? Compare and contrast the two. Tell which you prefer, and why.

Describe the kinds of movies you like and dislike.

Imagine that you are an usher cleaning the theater at the end of the day. Write a humorous story about a very unusual article that a movie-goer has left behind.

The Movie Theater

The Pizza Place

Describe pizza to an alien from outer space. Use sensory details to tell how it looks, smells, tastes, and feels.

Create a new topping combination for pizza. Then write a description suitable for the menu of the pizza parlor. Make your description so colorful that customers will want to order your original toppings on their pizza.

Imagine that you are the person who first created pizza. Very few people know that your discovery was strictly an accident. Write an article for a teen magazine in which you describe your accidental discovery of pizza while attempting to make something entirely different.

Write a humorous story about the owner of a pizza parlor who tries to set a new record for the world's largest pizza.

Imagine this pizza parlor fifty years from now. Describe the pizza of the future. In what ways will pizza be the same? In what ways will it be different?

Write a research report on the history of pizza. Include facts and details such as where it was first made, who is credited with its creation, etc. Use two or more sources of information.

Imagine that one of the girls in this picture has a cell phone in her pocket. The phone rings while she is eating. Describe the call. (The message is dramatic.)

Unexpected friends come into the restaurant, and one of them gets offended. Describe the conversation and the outcome.

The Pizza Place

The Tree House

To whom does this tree house belong? Write a short story using the tree house as part of the setting. Introduce two main characters, and include dialogue in your story.

Describe your favorite place to go when you want to be by yourself.

Write the first chapter of a suspense story called "The Tree House Mystery." Include well-developed details to enhance your plot.

If you could invite a famous person to join you in your tree house, whom would you select? What questions would you ask him or her?

If this were your tree house, describe how you would decorate the inside. What would you do to make it uniquely yours?

Describe the ways in which different seasons and weather affect how you feel and what you do in your tree house.

Imagine that you are the tree house. Use personification to describe the kids who come inside you to play.

The sign on the tree house reads: Private

The Tree House

The Library

Imagine that you are the teen at the computer in the picture. Describe your surroundings at the library.

Use sensory details to describe the silence of a library.

Imagine that you are the reference librarian at this library. Make a list of the most unusual and humorous questions kids have asked you over the years.

Write a humorous story about an undisciplined child who runs around the library screaming and yelling, shattering the peace and silence.

Imagine that you are a book sitting on a library shelf. Use personification to tell about a person who picks you off the shelf, checks you out of the library, and takes you home. What is this person like? Write a vivid character description.

Describe the best book you have ever read. What made this book so special?

Write a humorous story about a person who wins an award for returning the most overdue book in the library's history.

If you could be any character in a book you've read, whom would you choose to be? Why?

The Library

The Shoe Store

Imagine that you are a shoe like one of those pictured here. Using personification, write a first-person account about a typical day in your life from the time you are put on by your owner until the time he or she takes you off at night.

Write a humorous story about a mother who comes into a shoe store with a screaming child in tow. Write the dialogue between the frustrated mother and the shoe salesperson.

Write a short story based on the life of the person who is wearing one of the shoes pictured.

Imagine that you have been hired to write descriptions of each of these shoes for a catalog. Write a paragraph describing each shoe. Describe its comfort, the material it's made from, and its style.

Write a mystery that takes place in a shoe store. Include well-chosen details to develop the plot of your story. Use sensory details to paint vivid scenes.

Write an original version of the story of Cinderella, but substitute one of these shoes for the glass slipper.

Write a story about an overly ambitious shoe salesperson who tries to sell you a pair of shoes you really don't want or need. Write the dialogue between the two of you.

Describe your most "comfy" pair of shoes.

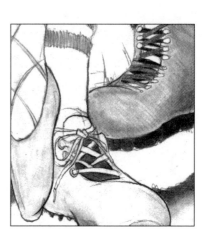

The Shoe Store

Amusement Park

Imagine that you are the person who runs the roller coaster ride at the amusement park. Write two paragraphs, one describing the girls before they got on the ride, and another describing them at the end of the ride. Compare and contrast the "before" and "after."

Imagine that you are one of the people on the roller coaster at an amusement park. Describe the wild ride you take, from the minute you take off until the cars come to a stop. Use sensory details to capture the sounds, smells, sights, and sensations you experience on the ride.

Write a mystery that takes place in an amusement park late at night. Use the roller coaster as part of the setting of your story.

Write an essay about a time you visited an amusement park. Tell where it was located, when you went, who went with you, and whether the visit was for a special occasion. Describe your favorite ride at the park.

Imagine that you are an engineer and have been selected to design a new amusement park ride that will appeal especially to teenagers. Write a one-page description of the ride you would design.

Write a research report about a well-known amusement park. Develop your topic with facts, details, examples, and explanations.

Write a persuasive letter to the editor of a newspaper stating your position in support of or against closing a roller coaster ride in an amusement park where several serious accidents have occurred.

Choose three or more of the following feelings and include them in a story about your experiences in an amusement park: fear, excitement, frustration, happiness, fatigue, exhilaration, embarrassment.

43

Amusement Park

Fences

What is the girl thinking about as she looks over the fence? Capture her mood and thoughts using sensory words to describe what she is seeing, hearing, smelling, and feeling as she stands by the fence.

What does the girl's expression and stance tell you about her feelings at this moment?

What brought this girl to the fence? Where will she go and what will she do when she leaves?

Instead of a wooden fence, imagine the girl is looking through a chain-link fence. Where is the fence located? What is behind it? Describe what the girl sees.

Imagine you are the person at the fence. Write four or five sentences describing the sounds you hear. For example, the sounds could be of children on a playground behind you, or traffic on the street in front of you. Use vivid words to capture all the sounds you hear.

Imagine that this girl is looking for her lost cat. Write a short story about her run-away pet.

Besides fences, what are other barriers that separate people from one another? Write a short story about someone your age who faces a crisis in his or her life. Include a fence or other barrier somewhere in your story.

Imagine that you are the fence. Using personification, write three or more para-graphs, each describing a different person you see during the day—including the girl in this picture.

Fences

Riding the Waves

Imagine that you are the person in the picture. Describe the emotions you experience as you ride the wave in to shore. Use colorful adjectives to make your description come alive. For example, you could describe how the sun feels beating down on your shoulders, or how the ocean spray feels on your face. Include the sights, smells, sounds, and tastes you experience while riding your surfboard.

Write from the perspective of two friends sitting on the beach watching the surfer catch a wave. Write a one-page conversation between them that expresses their thoughts and emotions. Try to make the dialogue between the friends sound real. Use slang or other expressions people their age would use.

Think back to the first time you tried a new sport, and write about your experience. Try to capture the emotions you felt that first time. Describe how you felt when you finished, and what you learned about yourself.

Write a short story about a surfer who gets caught in a powerful undertow. Describe the panic the surfer feels while being pulled under by the strong current. Describe the thoughts that race through his or her mind.

Write an action story about a lifeguard who comes to the rescue of a surfer in trouble. Write a strong introductory paragraph. Establish and support a central idea for your story with a topic sentence at or near the beginning of each paragraph. Conclude your narrative with a solid ending that shows resolution of your plot.

Imagine that you are the wave in the picture. Using personification, write in first person and describe yourself. Compare your motion and force to something else in nature. Tell why you are both loved and feared.

Write a poem about a surfer. Your poem does not have to rhyme.

Riding the Waves

A Work of Art

Describe the boy's thoughts as he views this sculpture at the Museum of Modern Art. What does he think the sculpture represents? What does it remind him of? How would he describe the sculpture to his friends?

Imagine that you are an art critic who has been asked to write a review of the sculpture for your local newspaper. Write a one-page critique of the sculpture, giving your opinion of the work.

Imagine that you are the sculptor who created this piece of art. Describe where the idea for the piece came from and how it evolved as you worked on it. What did you name this piece, and how did you come up with the name? Tell about your background as an artist, and mention awards you have won.

Imagine that you are this sculpture. You have been on display at the Museum of Modern Art for six months. Using personification, describe the three most unusual people who have stopped to look at you. What did they have to say about you?

Select one of the famous sculptors below, or choose one of your own. Do research to learn about that person's life, work, and artistic style. Write a research report that presents facts, details, examples, and explanations of the sculptor's work. Use two or more sources of information.

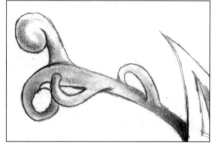

    Frederic Auguste Bartholdi
    Alexander Calder
    Henry Moore
    François Rodin

What is creativity? Write a one-page essay on this topic, expressing your personal views.

A Work of Art

Four Doors

Select one of the doors in the picture. Write a short story in which you describe in detail what's behind the door. Is it a place that is frightening or friendly? Historical, futuristic, or contemporary? Serious or humorous?

Choose one of the four doors and imagine stepping through and looking around. What do you see? Use sensory details to describe what's behind the door. Capture the mood, sounds, smells, and things you see.

Write a description of a person who lives behind one of these four doors. Describe his or her physical features, such as his or her hair, eyes, nose, hands, feet, and build. Describe how he or she is dressed. Describe the unique behavior or habits of your character.

Imagine that you are one of these four doors. Using personification, describe three very different people who have crossed your threshold.

Pick two of these doors, and write an imaginary conversation between them.

Write a short story based on a door to

> a haunted house
> a colonial home
> an old wooden shack
> an airplane
> a jail cell
> any door of your choice

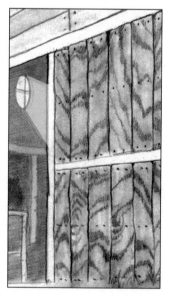

Select a famous building such as the White House, the Capitol, the Supreme Court, or a famous art or history museum. Imagine that you have been hired as a tour guide to tell visitors fascinating facts about the building as they step inside. Do research to learn about the history and other interesting facts about the building you selected. Write a report that you could use as a guide for tourists visiting the building.

Four Doors

Secrets

What secret is the one girl telling the other? Write an imaginary conversation between the two girls.

Has a friend ever betrayed your trust and shared a secret of yours with others? If so, describe how you felt. Did you confront your friend? Did it change the way you felt about your friend? Was any damage done by your secret getting out? How was the situation resolved?

Write a short story based on a secret that ended up hurting another person. Include well-developed details to constuct the plot of your story.

What would you do if your best friend confided in you and asked you to keep a secret that he or she was abusing drugs or alcohol? Would you break your friend's confidence in order to get help for him or her? Why or why not?

Write a mystery that has the word "Secret" in the title.

Use personification and make a secret take on the characteristics of a human being. Describe how you have the ability to bring both joy and sadness to other people.

Write a humorous story about a simple secret told to one person that gets blown way out of proportion, causing havoc in a middle school.

Plan the perfect surprise party for a friend. Describe where it would be and how you'd get your friend to the party. Also describe the theme, decorations, music, and food you'd plan for the surprise party. If you wish, you can even create a party invitation.

Copyright © 2003 The Learning Works

Secrets

It's About Time

Write a narrative about a time you were late for an important event. In your story, establish a plot, point of view, setting, and conflict. Describe the circumstances that made you late. What were the consequences of your not being on time?

Imagine that you are one of the clocks shown in the picture. Using personification, write a short story about your life. Include a description of the person who owns you. Tell how you came into his or her possession. Write about your life and something unusual that has happened to you.

 Write a science fiction story about the day time stood still. In your story, describe how people from various walks of life were affected.

Imagine that you have been selected to write ad copy for one of the clocks or watches pictured. Your ad will appear in a national magazine read by millions of people. Write descriptive copy about the timepiece pointing out all its unusual features.

Write a humorous story about someone your age who can't fall asleep because of a clock that is ticking too loudly. Create a unique solution to his or her problem.

What is your favorite time of day? Is it sunrise, when a new day is beginning and most people are still asleep and everything is tranquil? Is it noontime, a time filled with the hustle-bustle of people, noises, and traffic? Or is it sunset, when the sun is sinking in the sky at the end of the day? Write an essay describing your favorite time of day. Use vivid adjectives to capture the sounds, smells, sights, tastes, and feelings of this slice of time.

It's About Time

The Gift

Choose one of the gifts shown or imagine a different one you received. Write a paragraph describing what is inside. Make your description so detailed that some-one reading your paragraph can guess what's inside without your ever mentioning the item by name.

Describe a special gift you once received. Write an essay telling about the person who gave it to you, the occasion, and the gift itself. What made it so special?

Imagine that inside a gift you receive is one of the following character traits, which will be yours for one day to share with someone else:

    honesty
    tolerance
    courage
    compassion
    responsibility

Which of these gifts would you most like to receive? Write a narrative about the day this gift arrived and how you put it to use.

Write a short story about a gift that someone receives that takes him or her on an unexpected adventure. Develop the plot and setting for your story.

Write a humorous story about someone who receives a not-so-wonderful present and what he or she does with the unwanted gift.

Imagine that you are a copywriter who has been assigned the task of writing a description of one of the following gifts for a holiday catalog:

      a microwave oven
      a scooter
      a sports shoe
      a watch

If you prefer, you can select a different gift to describe. In your catalog copy, include a general description of the gift you select, and describe special features, colors, sizes, price, etc.

The Gift

The Time Machine

Imagine that you could step into this time machine and be transported back in time to any period of history. Would you choose to be part of an early civilization such as the Maya, Inca, or Aztec; set sail with the Vikings; fight in the American Revolution; travel by covered wagon during the westward expansion; or visit feudal Japan? Pick any period of history, and do research to learn all you can about it. Then write about one day in your life incorporating as many facts and details as you can.

Imagine that you could travel back in time and spend one day with a famous person who is no longer living. The time machine makes it possible to come face-to-face with any president, athlete, movie star, scientist, musician, or other famous person who has ever lived. Tell who you would visit and why you selected this man or woman. Then write a dialogue based on twelve or more questions you would ask and answers you think this person would give you.

Take a trip in the time machine and visit the world of the future. Write a description of the homes, modes of transportation, fashion, entertainment, medical break-throughs, and other phenomena of the future you see.

Write a science fiction story based on the experiences of a person who travels to another time and place. Use sensory details to capture the sights, sounds, smells, tastes, and feelings of this place and time.

Imagine that two best friends are on a field trip to a science lab. After stepping inside the time machine to look around, they hit one of the buttons to see what will happen. Suddenly, lights begin to swirl, buzzers begin to ring, and they find themselves hurled into another time. Write a humorous story about their wild adventure.

Imagine that it is the year 2050, and science is so advanced that time machines are going on sale to the public for the first time. You have been hired to write copy for a one-page ad describing this contraption. The ad will appear on Web sites and on-line magazines. Write descriptive copy so that everyone will want to rush out and buy time machines for their homes.

The Time Machine

Pets

Write an essay about an animal you have had or known. It may be your own pet; an animal belonging to a friend, neighbor, or relative; or a wild creature you have observed. Include descriptions of the animal's appearance, behavior, and personality.

If you don't have a pet, write a letter to your mom or dad telling her or him all the reasons why you should have a pet.

Sometimes kids can tell their problems to a pet more easily than to a person. Pretend the boy in the drawing is talking to his pet about a problem he is having at home or at school. Write the boy's conversation with his puppy.

 Imagine that you are a reporter for a local newspaper. You have been assigned to write a story about how this boy and his dog solved a crime in the neighborhood and became local heroes. Write a one-page story that will capture the hearts of your readers. Be sure to answer these questions: who, where, when, what, and how.

Imagine that you and your family have just adopted this puppy from the local animal shelter. Write a story describing what made you choose this puppy from among all the puppies at the shelter.

Write a short story from the point of view of the dog. Using personification, tell how you feel about the boy in the picture, what a typical day is like for you, about a time you got into serious trouble, or whatever you wish.

Describe a time when you did something to help a pet. Did you act alone, or were others involved? How do you think the animal felt?

Imagine that you are going to buy an iguana for a pet. Your mom and dad insist that you learn all you can about iguanas. Do some research on this reptile, and write a report filled with facts and details about the care and feeding of iguanas. Use two or more sources of information.

Pets

The Wheelchair

To whom does this wheelchair belong? Is the person a child, a teenager, or a senior citizen? What circumstances caused this person to be confined to a wheelchair? Write a short story about this person, and include the wheelchair in your story.

Make a list of ten or more things you do on a typical day, from the time you wake up to the time you go to bed at night. Then imagine that you had to spend the day in a wheelchair. Write an essay explaining how you would have to modify your daily activities to accommodate your wheelchair. What difficulties do you think you would encounter?

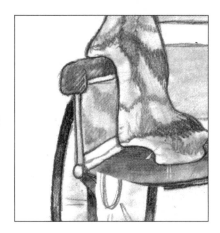

Imagine that you are a newspaper reporter. You have been assigned to research and write a story about a famous person who overcame a physical disability and accomplished something great. Franklin Roosevelt, Stephen Hawking, Itzhak Perlman, Helen Keller, and Stevie Wonder are just a few examples of people who have made great contributions to society despite their physical disabilities. Write a one-page report for your newspaper on the man or woman you select. Use two or more resources as you seek information.

Create a new outdoor sport that could be played by a person in a wheelchair. Describe the rules of play as well as the equipment that is needed. Draw and label diagrams to enhance your description.

Write a persuasive letter to the editor of your local newspaper, appealing for more accessible accommodations for people in wheelchairs. Your appeal could be for more parking spaces for the disabled, more accessible restrooms in public buildings and restaurants, or ramps to better accommodate wheelchairs on city sidewalks. State a clear position, and present relevant evidence in support of your proposal.

Do you know someone who uses a wheelchair? Pretend it's his or her birthday and volunteer to decorate the wheelchair with him or her in honor of the occasion. Write a description of how you would decorate the wheelchair without interfering with its movement. Think about the person and his or her hobbies, special interests, and favorite colors. If you don't know anyone who uses a wheelchair, decorate a wheelchair for someone your age. Have fun, and let your imagination soar!

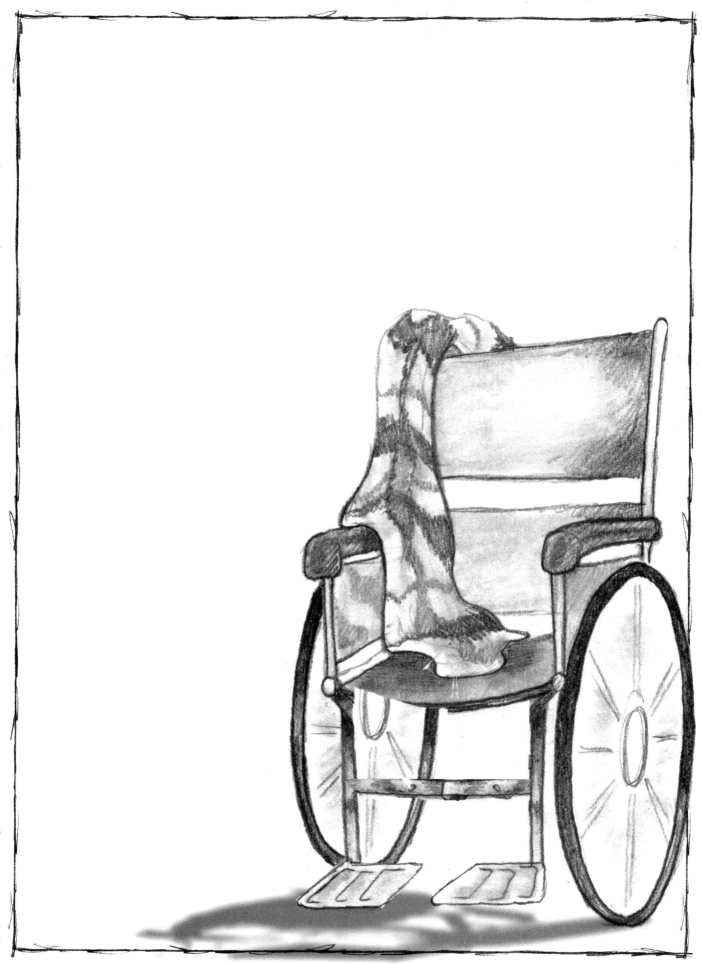

The Wheelchair

Happiness

The expressions on these kids' faces makes it very clear what they are feeling. Choose one of the three kids, and write a few sentences describing the way his or her emotions are shown through the eyes, eyebrows, and mouth.

Why are these kids happy? Write a short story describing the events that led up to this moment.

Write an essay describing the happiest day of your life. Describe all the things that made this day so special.

If happiness were a color, what color would it be? Write a paragraph in which you describe happiness as a color. Use comparisons and descriptive words to convey your ideas.

List ten things that make you happy. Include five or more of these things in an essay on happiness.

Who is the happiest person you know? Is this person happy because his or her life has been easy, or despite problems and conflicts? Use sensory details to describe his or her personality and laugh.

Write a paragraph or two describing something nice you did for another person that made him or her happy.

Write a haiku poem about happiness. Your poem should have three lines. The first line should have five syllables, the second line seven syllables, and the third line five syllables.

65

Happiness

Anger

The players in the picture are angry. Think of something that might have triggered this conflict. Imagine that you are the player on the left and write about what happened to make you so angry, as though you were explaining the incident to a referee. Then take the identity of the player on the right. Write about the same incident from this person's point of view.

Think about a time when you were angry. Remember how you felt. Now bring those feelings back, and be aware of how they affected you physically. How does anger change your eyes, nose, mouth, neck, and hands? Write an essay describing how anger affects the way you look and feel.

Write about anger in the first person, as if you were anger. Begin your essay with "I am Anger." Use personification to tell about yourself—what sets you off, how you express yourself, and how you affect others.

Write a myth about two creatures who learn how to deal with their anger.

What color is anger? Write a paragraph describing anger as if it were a color. Use at least two similes in your writing.

Write about a time when you were very angry. Who or what were you angry at? What circumstances led to the incident? Was the issue ever resolved?

Draw a cartoon and write captions showing how two characters deal with anger.

Write a poem about anger. Your poem does not have to rhyme.

Anger

Love

How do the people in your family express their love for you—in words, or by the things they do for you? Write an essay about ways love is expressed in a family.

Put into words this father's love for his infant son.

There are many different kinds of love. Select any of the following to describe or to use as the basis for a short story:

      a child's love of an animal
      a child's love of a parent
      love of family
      love between friends
      love of a sport or hobby
      love of nature

Write a story from the baby's point of view. How does he feel as he is held by his father?

Write a letter to someone in your family, telling how much you love him or her. Let this person know how much you appreciate all the things he or she does for you and how much you care.

Write a poem about love in which each line has exactly two words. Your poem does not have to rhyme.

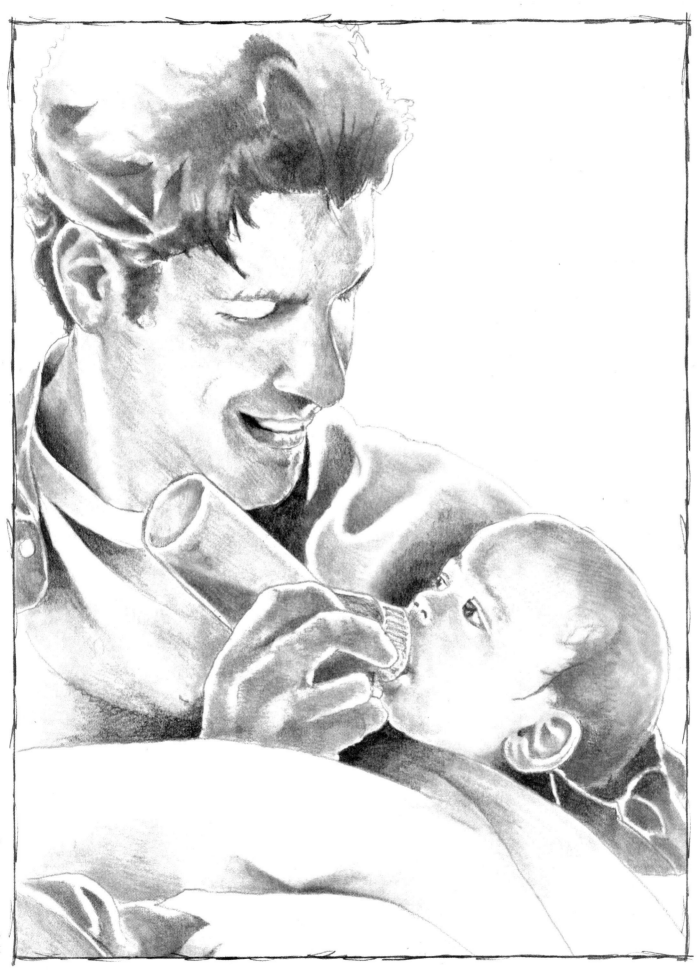

Love

Disappointment

Write a short story based on the picture, and describe the thoughts and feelings of the boy in the background.

Write an essay about a major disappointment in your life. Describe the events that led up to the disappointment, and tell what you learned from the experience.

Write about a person who disappointed you and let you down when you were counting on him or her.

Write a short story about someone who wants something very badly and is extremely disappointed when he or she doesn't get it. But make your story have a happy ending in which everything happens for the best in the long run.

Write a short story about someone who competes in a contest and loses. Use any of the following situations, or create one of your own:

> a spelling bee
> a race
> a debate
> a sporting event
> a dance contest

How do people handle disappointment differently? Describe how someone you know reacted to disappointment. Would you react similarly? Why or why not?

Disappointment

Fear

Imagine that the boy in the picture is home alone and hears someone creeping outside his bedroom window. Write a short story that captures the fear he feels. Include all the senses in describing his fear.

Think back to a time when you were extremely frightened. What were the circumstances that led to the incident? Write an essay describing the fear you felt and how it affected you.

Write a scary story that could be told at a sleepover or around a campfire. Make your story scary enough to make goosebumps appear on those who hear your spooky tale.

What color is fear? Write a paragraph describing fear as if it were a color. Use similes in your description.

Some children are afraid of the dark. Many adults are afraid to fly in airplanes. Other people are afraid of snakes, spiders, or insects. Write a short story about someone who faces and overcomes a fear.

Write a narrative about a scary dream you had. Include well-chosen details to develop your personal account.

Learning something new can be an unsettling experience. Whether it's learning to ski, ride a horse, or solve geometry problems, things can be scary until you acquire the necessary skills. Write an essay about something you tried that was frightening at first.

Write a short story about a student who overcomes his or her fear of speaking in front of the class. Use sensory details to present and support impressions of your main character and his or her experience.

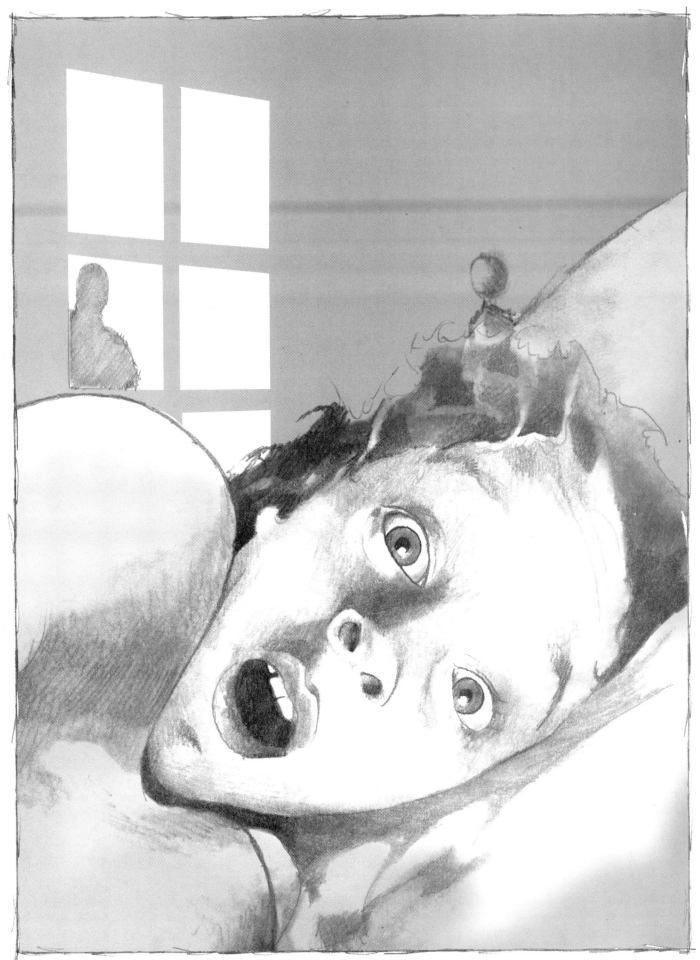

Fear

Loneliness

Imagine you are the girl sitting by herself on the far side of the room. Describe the feelings you have as you observe the party going on all around you.

Describe a time when you felt lonely even though you were surrounded by other people.

Write an essay describing steps you take to help you beat the blues when you're feeling lonely.

Describe a time when you reached out to someone at school who seemed lonely, or when someone reached out to you.

Use the school cafeteria as the setting for a short story about loneliness. In your story, use sensory details to present and support impressions of people, places, things, and experiences.

Write a short story about a person who moves to a new community and has a difficult time fitting into the social scene at school. At the end of your story, show how the issue is resolved.

Write a poem about loneliness. Your poem does not have to rhyme.

Loneliness

Sadness

Write a short story using the teenager in the drawing as the main character. In your story, tell about the events that brought him to this scene. Who is the other person in the picture? What is the connection between the two?

Sadness is often associated with loss. Write about the loss of a friend, family member, or pet. Describe the various emotions you felt. What helped you through this experience?

Write about a friend or family member who was there for you when you felt sad.

Sadness is often followed closely by happiness. Describe a time when you felt sad and the situation suddenly changed to make you happy. Give details about how your feelings affected you physically and emotionally.

Write a poem about sadness by completing each of these thoughts

    Sadness is like…
    Sadness reminds me of the color _____ because…
    Sadness is found…
    Sadness sounds like…
    Sadness lives…
    Sadness looks like…
    Sadness makes me feel…

Use personification, and write a story about sadness as if it were a person.

Sadness

Jealousy

Imagine that you are the boy in the picture. You are walking home from school and feel jealous of the high school students you see driving around the neighborhood in a brand-new car. Describe the thoughts that go through your mind.

Describe a time when you were jealous of someone else. What made you jealous? How did it make you feel?

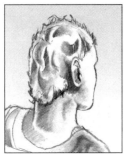

Write about two siblings who are constantly jealous of each other.

Write a short story about a person who is jealous because of something that another person owns. The possession could be a piece of jewelry, an article of clothing, or anything you want it to be.

Jealousy is sometimes referred to as a green-eyed monster. Write a humorous story about this monster on the loose and how it affects the life of someone your age.

Using personification, write about jealousy in the first person. Describe how you affect people and how you make them feel.

Write a poem about jealousy, and include a simile using "like" or "as" to compare jealousy to something else.

Jealousy

Student Checklist

Use this checklist when you have completed the first draft of your writing.

☐ I have checked my writing for spelling errors.

☐ I have used correct capitalization.

☐ I have used punctuation marks such as colons, semicolons, and quotation marks correctly.

☐ I have used verb tenses correctly and have read my writing over for grammatical errors.

☐ When writing a research report, I have used more than one source of information.

☐ When writing a research report, I have provided facts, examples, and explanations to clarify my topic.

☐ I have started my writing with a strong opening paragraph that sets the tone of the piece.

☐ Each paragraph of my piece has a well-defined topic sentence and supporting details.

☐ I have used sensory details in my writing.

☐ I have a well-written closing paragraph.